chick

teddy

KU-165-407

girl

bag

bowl

fairy

bed

eel

cat

hat

caterpillar

spaceship

mirror

sheep

tiara

Contents

First published 2016 by Brown Watson
The Old Mill, 76 Fleckney Road
Kibworth Beauchamp
Leicestershire LE8 0HG

ISBN: 978 0 7097 2364 6

© 2016 Brown Watson, England

Reprinted 2017

Printed in Malaysia

My First
1000
Words & Pictures

Brown Watson

ENGLAND

ens

notebook

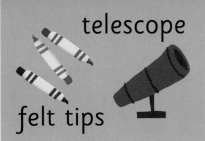
drawing

telescope
felt tips

dinosaur
headphones

ballet shoes

beanbag

ball

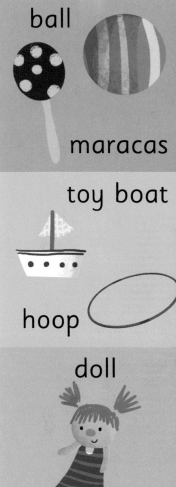

maracas

toy boat

hoop

doll

soft toys

stacking
rings

drums

13

BATHROOM

 scales

soap dish

mirr

water

toilet

shower

bath towel

shampoo

mouthwash

toothbrush

toothpaste

rubber duck

14 bubbles

am

cheese
apples

pears

milk
strawberries

checkout

broccoli
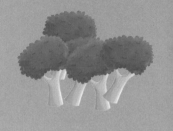

onions
carrots

basket

eggs

cucumber

cabbage

shopping
bags

27

OUTSIDE

butterfly

skipping rope

swings

leaf

sur

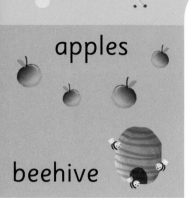
apples

beehive

worm

plane

fountain

fence

bees

crow

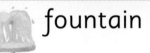
slide

28 playground

hell

sunglasses

ice cream

starfish

deckchair

palm tree

swimming costume

desert island

rubber ring

flip-flops

inflatable

armbands

paddling

sea

sunbathing

windbreak

beach bag

41

PARTY TIME

present

crisps

juice

cupcake

gir

balloon

drink

sandwiches

straw

cookie

ice cream

birthday cake

candles

guests

Happy
Birthday

42

rab

jellyfish

starfish

anchor

seal

diver

flippers

octopus

tentacles

treasure chest

gold

turtle

seahorse

49

STORYBOOK WORDS

wizard

ogre

fairy

witch

princess

prince

unicorn

knight

castle

drawbridge

king

dragon

queen

magic wand

50

palace

sword

pixie

gold

shield

sceptre

throne

barrels

ghost

time machine

flying carpet

pirate ship

crown

monster

pirate

cannon

cannon balls

51

Disney's

Bambi

Ladybird

One spring morning, just as the sun was rising, animals and birds hopped, scurried and fluttered to a quiet thicket in the middle of the forest. As they went, they spread the exciting news: "The new Prince is born! Come and see!"

The new Prince was a small, spotted fawn, the son of the noble stag who was the Great Prince of the Forest. All the animals and birds gathered round to admire the new baby as he slept by his mother's side.

"Congratulations," they said to Mother Deer.

"Thank you," she said, gently nuzzling her fawn.

"What will you call him?" asked a young rabbit named Thumper.

"Bambi," replied Mother Deer, and all the animals nodded.

It wasn't long before Bambi was ready to explore the forest with his mother. Each day they walked through the wood, and all the animals and birds greeted them.

"Good morning, Bambi! Good morning, young Prince!" chirped Mother Quail and her nine babies.

Bambi learned that the forest was a fascinating place, and that he had friends all around him.

Bambi soon made a special friend – Thumper the rabbit. Thumper showed him all the best places to play, and taught him how to hop over logs.

Thumper also taught Bambi to say his first word – *bird*. Bambi was so proud of himself that he said it over and over: "Bird, bird, bird!" he cried happily.

When Bambi saw a bright yellow butterfly fluttering through the air, he called, "Bird!"

"No," said Thumper, "that's a butterfly!"

"Butterfly!" repeated Bambi, as he leapt into a bed of white and yellow flowers.

"No, that's a flower!" laughed Thumper. He sniffed one. "It's pretty," he told Bambi.

"Flower," said Bambi, as he bent to sniff the flowers too. Suddenly a little black-and-white head popped up from under the flowers.

"Flower!" said Bambi again.

Thumper giggled. "That's not a flower, that's a skunk!" he said.

"That's all right," said the little skunk shyly. "He can call me Flower if he wants to!"

Bambi had made another friend.

One day Bambi's mother took him to a very special place – the meadow.

The meadow was wide and open, with no trees for protection, so they had to be very careful. Bambi's mother went ahead to make sure there was no danger, then she called Bambi to come to her.

Bambi loved the meadow. It was so much fun to run and leap across the open spaces, and the tall grass tickled his legs.

There were other deer in the meadow too, and one of them was a fawn just the same age as Bambi. She came up to Bambi and wagged her tail in friendship.

Bambi had never seen another fawn before. Overcome with shyness, he rushed back to his mother and tried to hide.

"It's all right, Bambi," his mother assured him. "That's Faline. She just wants to be friends with you. Go and say hello."

Timidly, Bambi went back to Faline. She giggled and began chasing him. Bambi couldn't resist chasing her in return. Soon the two fawns were laughing and skipping together, enjoying an exciting game of hide-and-seek in the rushes. Their mothers watched them happily.

All at once, Bambi and Faline heard the thunder of hoofbeats. They clambered up onto a rock and saw a large group of stags charging across the meadow. The herd bounded through the grass, leaping far and high as they ran.

Bambi followed the galloping stags until they stopped suddenly. There in front of them was a very tall deer, with many-branched antlers. It was the Great Prince of the Forest. He walked towards Bambi, looking proudly at his son.

The Great Prince had come to warn the animals that danger was near.

All the deer raced towards the trees. Faline's mother rushed to her daughter's side and they ran together to safety. Bambi could not find his own mother and started to panic. But there beside him was the Great Prince, pointing out the way to go. Bambi ran with him into the wood and was overjoyed to find his mother running with them too.

Back in the safety of the thicket, Bambi asked his mother what the danger had been.

"Man was in the forest," was all she replied. She was very glad that the hunters and their guns had gone – for now.

One morning when Bambi awoke, the world was covered in a white blanket.

"It's snow, Bambi," his mother told him. "Winter has come."

Suddenly, Bambi heard Thumper calling him. He looked up and saw Thumper sliding across the pond.

Bambi ran down onto the frozen pond and landed – *SPLAT!* – right on his tummy! Thumper laughed and tried to help his friend glide across the ice. Soon Bambi was whizzing along.

Winter was a happy time at first, but Bambi soon learned that it was a difficult time as well. The deer had to spend all their time searching for food, which was growing scarce. One day when the air seemed a bit warmer, Bambi and his mother went to the meadow to look for food. There they found a little patch of green peeping through the snow.

"It's new spring grass," Bambi's mother said. "This means that winter will be over before too long."

Suddenly Bambi's mother looked up. She sensed danger nearby.

"Go to the thicket," she told Bambi. "Quickly! Run!"

Bambi raced across the meadow. All at once he heard a loud *BANG!*

"Faster, Bambi!" called his mother, right behind him. "Run, and don't look back!"

The fear in her voice made Bambi frightened, too, and he ran even faster. Suddenly there was another *BANG*, louder than the first. Terror surged through him as he tore through the forest, desperate to reach home.

At last, in the shelter of the thicket, Bambi stopped. Breathless, he listened for his mother's hoofbeats behind him. But there was only silence.

"Mother!" he called. "Mother, where are you?"

There was no answer.

Bambi's heart thumped with panic as he looked around for his mother. "Mother, where are you?" he called again and again.

The Great Prince of the Forest came to Bambi's side.

"Your mother cannot be with you any longer," he said to Bambi.

Bambi began to cry, remembering the loud *BANG*. Man's guns had taken his mother from him for *ever*.

"Come, my son," said the Great Prince. "You must be brave and learn to walk alone now."

Staying close to his father, Bambi walked silently through the forest. He knew he would miss his mother, and he would remember her always.

The long, harsh winter ended at last, and spring returned to the forest. Leaves appeared on the trees, green shoots poked through the ground and flowers bloomed.

All the young animals were eager to see one another again. Thumper the rabbit hopped up onto a log and began thumping with his big foot.

"Bambi!" he called. "It's Thumper. Remember me?"

Flower's stripy head popped up from a patch of daisies. He had had a long sleep over the winter, and now he was rested and full of energy.

"Hi there, fellows!" he called. Like Thumper, he had grown bigger and had a deeper voice.

Bambi greeted his old friends happily. The spots had faded from his coat, and on his head he proudly carried a brand-new set of antlers.

As the three friends strolled through the wood together, Flower noticed a pretty female skunk smiling at him. Suddenly Flower felt tingly all over.

"Uh-oh," said Thumper. "Flower's twitterpated! Owl says it happens to everyone in springtime!"

"Well, it won't happen to me!" Bambi declared.

"Me neither!" agreed Thumper. But a moment later a lovely young female rabbit hopped up and said hello to him. Thumper gazed adoringly at her!

Bambi walked on alone. As he leant down for a drink at a pond he heard a soft voice beside him. "Hello Bambi. Don't you remember me? I'm Faline."

Bambi suddenly felt very awkward. He tried to back away, but his antlers got caught in a branch. Faline came closer and licked his face. Bambi winced, but then discovered he enjoyed it!

Bambi was so happy, he felt as if he were floating. Together, he and Faline walked through the forest towards the meadow where they had played as carefree young fawns.

All at once a strong young stag burst through the bushes. "You're not going any further," he said to Bambi. "Faline is coming with me!" He pushed Bambi out of the way and tossed his antlers at Faline. Then he drove her deeper into the wood, away from the young Prince.

"Bambi!" she cried, frightened and confused.

Bambi had never been in a fight before, but he could not let this rough bully harm Faline. Lowering his head, he charged at the other stag with all his might.

The two stags locked antlers and tossed one another this way and that. The stranger was strong and more experienced than Bambi, and with a powerful twist of his head, he flung Bambi to the ground.

But Bambi was determined not to be defeated, and he got up and charged again. His antlers crashed into the other stag's, and this time Bambi managed to throw him down.

Bambi waited for the other stag to get up and attack again. But the stranger limped away. Bambi had won. He and Faline could now be together.

Early one morning, a strange scent in the air woke Bambi. Careful not to wake Faline as she slept beside him, he left the thicket to find out what it was.

Standing on a cliff high above the wood, Bambi saw smoke rising from a clearing. His father came up beside him. "Man has returned," he told Bambi. "Those are his campfires. We must go deep into the forest – quickly!"

Bambi hurried away to warn Faline but she was not where he had left her. When she had woken up and found Bambi gone, she had panicked and run off to look for him.

"Bambi!" she cried, as she darted through the trees. All at once the sound of gunfire rang out, and a pack of hunting dogs came tearing through the wood. Faline ran quickly, but they bounded after her. Terrified, Faline climbed onto a rocky ledge. "Bambi!" she cried desperately, as the dogs leapt up at her.

Hearing her cries, Bambi sped towards Faline. He rushed at the pack of dogs, distracting them so that Faline could escape.

Bambi managed to fight the dogs off and make his own escape. But just when he thought he was safe, he heard a loud *BANG!*

A searing pain shot through Bambi's shoulder, and he fell to the ground. As he lay there, Bambi could smell smoke drifting closer and closer. The flames from Man's campfires were spreading. He knew he should get up, but he was too weak.

"Get up, Bambi!" said a deep voice above him. It was his father, the Great Prince of the Forest. "The forest is on fire," he said. "You must get up!"

Slowly, painfully, Bambi struggled to his feet.

"We must go to the lake," said the Great Prince. "Come with me."

As Bambi followed his father, his strength returned. Together they sprang this way and that to find a safe path through the blaze.

At last they reached the lake. In the middle was an island where many animals had already found safety. Bambi and his father swam towards it.

Safe on the island, Faline was waiting for them. She was so relieved and grateful to see that Bambi was alive! The forest creatures watched the flames sweep through their homes. They were glad to have escaped with their lives – but would there be anything to go back to when the fire died down?

They eventually returned to the forest and found their homes destroyed. But when spring came, green shoots sprang up once more.

One warm morning, Owl was awakened by a family of rabbits thumping loudly beneath his tree.

"Wake up, friend Owl!" called Thumper and his four children.

"Oh, what now?" asked Owl sleepily. "What's going on around here?"

But the rabbits were too excited to stay and explain.

Owl, wondering what all the excitement was about, followed their path as they scampered through the forest.

They were soon joined by Flower and his family, squirrels, raccoons, and chipmunks, all going in the same direction. Overhead, birds darted through the branches, chattering loudly.

"What's going on?" Owl asked again.

"It's happened!" said Flower. "In the thicket!"

As soon as Owl got to the thicket, he understood what all the fuss was about.

For there, surrounded by a crowd of admiring animals, was Faline. And snuggled close to her were two brand-new spotted fawns.

"Prince Bambi must be awfully proud!" said Owl.

Bambi was indeed very proud. He knew that he would love and protect Faline and their two fawns, just as his own father had loved and protected him – and all the forest creatures. For now he, Bambi, was the new Great Prince of the Forest, and he looked forward to the years ahead.